ASIAPAC COMIC

Origin
TIBE
CULTURE

西藏文化的故事

Illustrated by Feng Ge
Translated by Geraldine Goh

ASIAPAC • SINGAPORE

Publisher
ASIAPAC BOOKS PTE LTD
996 Bendemeer Road #06-09
Singapore 339944
Tel: (65) 6392 8455
Fax: (65) 6392 6455
Email: asiapacbooks@pacific.net.sg

Come visit us at our Internet home page
www.asiapacbooks.com

First published December 2002

ISBN 981-229-314-0

Cover illustration by Feng Ge
Cover design by Kelly Lim
Body text in 8/9pt Helvetica
Printed in Singapore by Chung Printing

Publisher's Note

Few people know the true face of Tibet. Situated 4,000 metres above sea level, in the untamed mountainous heartland of Asia, the Land of Snows is home to a people that the industrial age seems to have left behind.

Stepping into Tibet is like stepping back in time. Dancing, singing and opera performances are commonplace at religious and festive occasions, which are sometimes celebrated in the woods. Prayer flags, which signify good luck and fortune, greet you at every turn. The calm, weather-beaten features of the adults complement the fresh, eager faces of their youngsters. This is clearly a people who are truly at one with nature.

Yet Tibetans do not appear to be any worse for it. Seemingly oblivious to the rest of the world, they carry on with their unique way of life, practising customs and rituals that many outsiders find strange and bizarre. How else would you describe the belief that if vultures were to devour one's corpse, the sins of the past would be forgiven? Or what about the Bathing Festival, in which the rivers and streams were believed to contain medicinal qualities upon the appearance of a certain star?

This book is an enjoyable read, giving one a glimpse into the colourful legends and culture of the Tibetan people.

We would like to thank Feng Ge for his vivid illustrations, Geraldine Goh for her translation, Chua Wei Lin for providing editorial support, and the production team for putting in their best efforts in the publication of this book.

About the Illustrator

Feng Ge冯戈was born in 1973 in Yuechi of Sichuan Province, China. He graduated from the Art College of the Xinan Shifan University, specialising in oil painting.

He has loved drawing since his childhood days. In 1995, he started working on comics and has since produced *The Seven Lads of Yang*, *Celestial Eagle of the Snow*, *Flute Sage*, *The Curtain of Heaven Falls*, *The Sword of Sorrow*, and *Wild Goose on Goat's Sand*. He is currently working in a comics studio in Shanghai.

Contents

On the snowy peak,
A majestic monastery sits,
Enfolding the legends and history,
Of an age of desolation.

Yaks and goats on the barren land...
A brave and hard-working people has lived and multiplied in this remote and mysterious land, that has witnessed historical and natural changes over thousands of years. Here, we gain an insight into the land's unique landscape and its ancient customs.

TIBET: THE LAND OF SNOWS

Tibet is a starkly beautiful land long shrouded in mystery, unique in its natural conditions, language, traditions and culture. Situated at an average elevation of 4,000 metres above sea level and surrounded by lofty mountain ranges like the Himalayas and Kunlun Mountains, among others, it is no wonder that Tibet has been given such romantic names as "the Land of Snows" and "Rooftop of the World".

The Yarlung Tsangpo flowing through the Zetang district. In summer when the flood waters recede, a stretch of sand appears on the surface.

Although much of Tibet is generally dry, receiving only about 45 cm of rainfall annually, it is paradoxically also the source of some of Asia's greatest rivers: the Yangtse and the Yellow rivers in China, the Brahmaputra in India, the Salween in Burma, and the Mekong that passes through several Asian countries.

The Seven Tibetan Prefectures

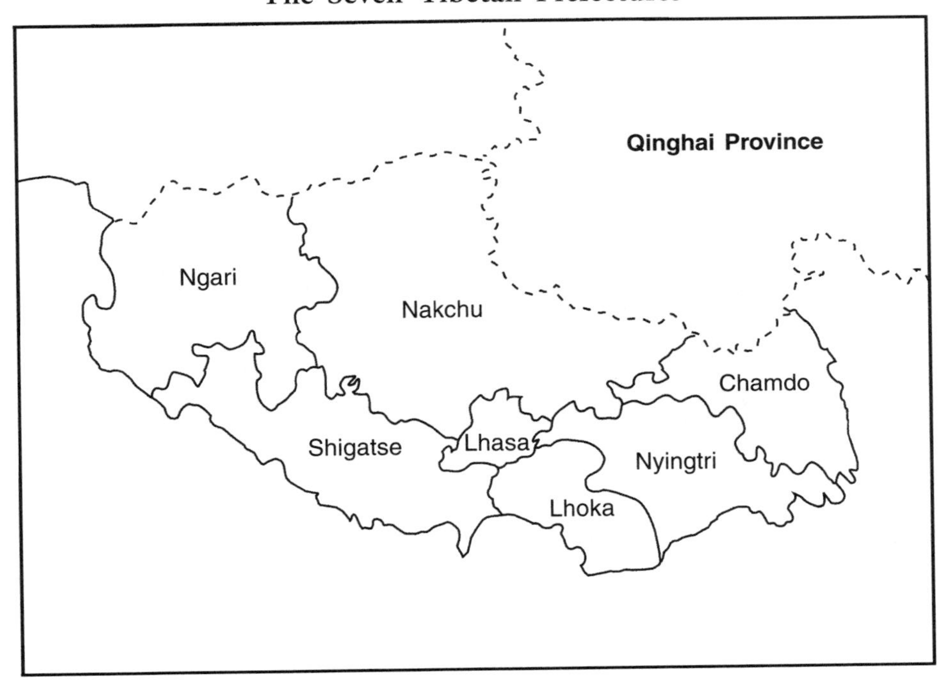

Regions

Tibet can be divided into three main regions.

The Northern Plain, called Changthang, is largely uninhabited desert that becomes extensive pastures and grasslands towards the south, home to a scattered population of nomads who live in tents and herd hardy domestic animals like yaks, sheep and goats.

Eastern Tibet is an area of steep mountains and valleys, where the Yangtse, Mekong and Salween, here known by their respective Tibetan names of Drichu, Zachu and Gyalmo Nyulchu, flow in deep, parallel gorges. Dense evergreen forests and grasslands cover much of this region, which lies at somewhat lower elevations than the rest of Tibet.

But it is in the valleys of the Tsangpo (Brahmaputra) river and its tributaries in the south of Tibet that most of the crops that the Tibetan people depend on are grown, and where much of the population lives. Here is where you find Lhasa, the ancient capital of Tibet, as well as the other great towns that serve as centres of trade and seats of government. This is the cradle of Tibetan culture and civilisation.

TIBETAN FOOD

Traditional Tibetan food is mainly barley, meat and dairy products, as vegetables and fish are rare at high altitudes.

The staple food is parched barley flour, called *tsampa*, which is eaten at every meal and carried as a convenient food for travel. The flour is placed in a bowl and salted butter tea, another cornerstone of the Tibetan diet, is added, mixed into small lumps and squeezed into the mouth with fingers. The salted tea is made by churning tea with salt and butter until it is well blended, and drunk throughout the day. The sour milk residue left from making butter is turned into milk curd, a good thirst quencher. The milk curd can also be made into pastry with the ubiquitous barley flour.

Another important food is yogurt, which has been eaten for over a millennium. Milk is first boiled, then some old yogurt is added after it is removed from the stove, and it will become yogurt in a few hours.

Meat, usually beef or mutton, can be cut into long strips and dried into crispy strips which are eaten raw, or boiled with salt and spices in large segments. Breasts and spareribs are offered to guests, and the guest of honour may be treated to a sheep's tail.

Other common foods are sausages, made from blood, meat, flour or liver; dumplings; noodles and yak tongue. Sweetened milk tea and mild barley beer are also popular alternative drinks to the salted butter tea.

The Tibetan New Year

Like other peoples of the world, the Tibetans regard the New Year as the most important festival of the year.

Eating *Gudusuo*

The family gathers round and enjoys the *gudusuo.*

Umm, it's salty.

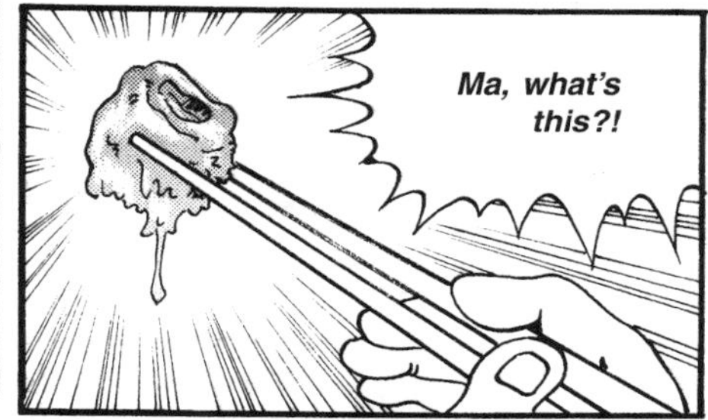
Ma, what's this?!

I added other things into the soup. What you eat is a reflection of your character and fortunes in life.

Ma, this is salt. What does it say about me?

You're a lazy person.

I've got a dried peach.

Pa, congratulations! This means you're still in very good health.

Ha ha! I do feel strong and healthy.

Ma, I got a strand of goat's hair.

It means you're a kind person.

Thank you, Ma!

Let me see what I've got.

There's a flour figure in my soup!

The one who gets the flour figure will suffer a forfeit!
Now make the sound of an animal first. Do you want to be a donkey or a dog?

Woof!
Woof!
Woof!

Ha ha ha...

Drink nine scoops of soup.

One, two!
Three, four!

Burp …
Five!

No… I can't drink any more.

Don't break the rules! If you don't drink it, we'll force-feed you!

Waah… No… No!
Ha ha ha…

Driving Away the Ghost

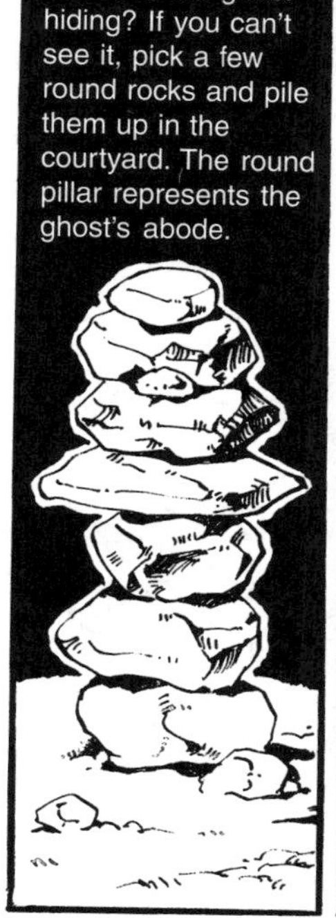

Ma then places the dough in a basin.

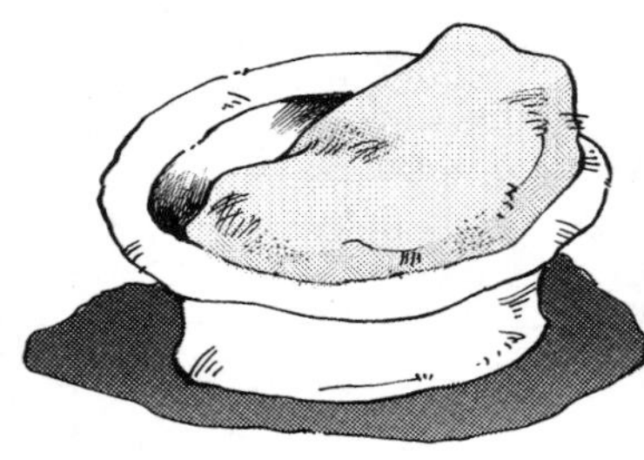

Mr Ghost,
you should
be full now.
Pow!

Come out!
Come out!
After kicking down the pile of stones, Pa runs out with the basin in his hands. He is followed by people carrying burning torches. They shout as they run.

On reaching the square, they light up the hay and break the ghost's rice bowl. Happily, they drink, sing and dance to celebrate their success in driving away the ghost. Perhaps they believe that the ghost will flee the world since his "rice bowl" has been broken.

TIBETAN DRESS

Both men and women often keep long hair in queues, with men having it coiled on top of the head, and adult women plaiting their hair into two or more queues adorned with ornaments. Some men may cut their hair short. They wear felt or fur hats, which differ from region to region.

Most Tibetans wear silk or cloth jackets with skirts for women and trousers for men, with a loose gown on top tied with a band on the right, and woollen or leather boots. One or both sleeves of the gown are often left off and tied around the waist for convenience when working, and in farming communities the gown may be sleeveless altogether. Herders wear sheepskin robes in place of the jacket. Men have long waistbands while women wear colourful aprons. Ornaments are popular among both sexes.

SOCIAL NICETIES

Address and greetings

Tibetans do not address people by name directly, preferring to attach an honorific. This honorific differs from region to region, with people in Lhasa adding the suffix "la", others adding the prefix "Agyi" or "Ajog" to men's names in Xigaze.

On meeting an elder or respected person, Tibetans take off their hats and bow, holding their hats low, close to the ground. It is enough to lower the head a little and hold the hat at the chest when meeting a peer.

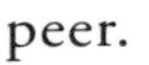

Proper behaviour and taboos

When visiting a Tibetan family, the host will offer barley wine, into which the guest should dip his fourth finger and flick three times for heaven, earth, and the ancestors. The guest should then take a sip and have his cup refilled three times. The third time the cup is refilled, the guest should empty the cup to avoid insulting the host.

While seated (on the floor with legs crossed), the host will prepare butter tea, which the guest should wait for the host to offer and not help himself. Gifts should be presented with a bow, holding the gift high above the head, and accepted with both hands. When offering wine or tea, the bowl should be held in both hands and fingers should not touch the brim.

Tibetans do not eat donkey, horse or dog meat, nor do they hunt or kill wildlife. In some regions, fish and birds are also anathema.

Religious structures and buildings like pagodas, monasteries and piles of mani stones must be walked around in a clockwise direction, just as prayer wheels are turned only clockwise, except for Bon monasteries, in which the reverse is true. Similarly, ritual utensils and other religious objects must be walked around, not stepped over.

The *Linka* Festival

During the fifth lunar month of the Tibetan calendar, Tibetans celebrate the *Linka* Festival from the first to the fifth day.

In Tibetan, *Linka* means a green world of water and trees.

Heaven has brought spring, warm sunshine, greenery and lush trees after the long harsh winter. Dressed to the nines, the Tibetans carry all kinds of delicious food with them to the woods for a picnic.

Tents are pitched by the riverside and in the green fields. People sing and dance. This is Tibet's *Linka* Festival.

The celebration held in Shigatse is the most orthodox. There is a moving story about the *Linka* Festival.

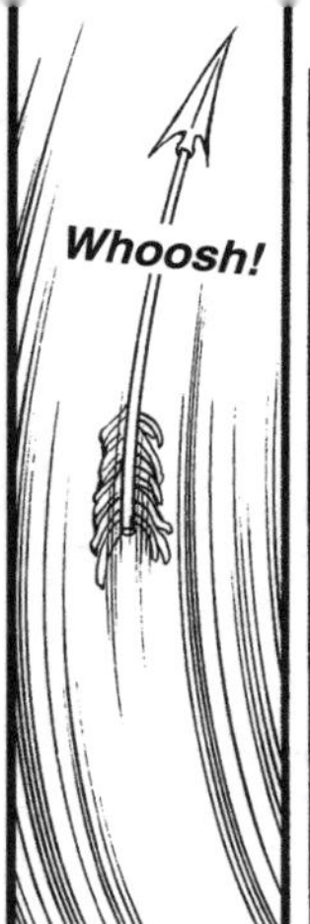
Whoosh!

Screech!

Pak!

Tudengnima, you're a great marksman!

We've been hunting all morning. Shall we find a place to rest?
Ja...
Good idea! Let's roast the eagle.
The hunters found a cave by the hillside.
We'll rest in the cave.
All right.

Om mani padme hum…

I can smell roast meat!

It's from the cave.

Wow… Smells really good. We can eat it now.
Oh, it's delicious!

What are you doing?!

Snort...

Ma'am, why are you so angry?

Who permitted you to make this place all smoky? Do you know where you are?

This is just a cave.

It isn't an ordinary cave. This is Gabujia Cave. When Guru Rinpoche came to Tibet from India to spread the faith, he stayed here for a year to meditate.
This is a sacred place.

Guru Rinpoche's original name was Padmasambhava. He was a Buddhist master from *Wuzhangna* (present-day Pakistan) and was an expert in destroying evil spirits. He was well-known for his magical powers.
Guru Rinpoche came to Tibet to spread Buddhism at the invitation of the Tibetan king.
In those days, the people followed the native animistic religion known as Bon.
The followers of Bon were very unhappy with Guru Rinpoche's visit.

Guru Rinpoche's wisdom lay in his ability to learn from his ancestors and to merge the gods of nature into Buddhism.

He accepted the local spirits and the 12 *Danma* as the guardian gods of Buddhism.

One day, Guru Rinpoche came to a building site and noticed that the craftsmen were all looking sad and depressed.

Why are you so unhappy?

Guru, evil spirits have been harassing us.

Where do the evil spirits come from? Tell me.

Long ago, an Indian priest named Reverend Jingming came to our land to spread the faith.
He came to Samye and saw at once that it was a sacred place. He decided to build a monastery here.

The work began, but each time the monastery was built, it would fall apart. The builders grew afraid, believing that the evil dragon in the river was making trouble.

Guru Rinpoche came to the river and chanted.
Whoosh!
Ting-a-ling-ling...
Bloow!

Guru Rinpoche destroyed the evil dragon, and work on the monastery resumed. Some 20 years later, the first monastery of Tibet was built. It is the Samye Monastery.

Guru Rinpoche proclaimed King Trisong Detsen the son of an immortal. The king thought highly of him and Buddhism flourished.

We worship this place as it is sacred ground.

Yet you're doing things that will offend the spirits.

Guru, we didn't know you had meditated in this cave. We've done wrong and are sorry.
Forgive these ignorant people, Guru.

The next day, the three hunters brought other people to Gabujia Cave to pray.

Their wives and children brought food and gathered in the woods near their homes to welcome the return of their close ones. They would bring back good fortune after praying to the Guru.

Men and women fervently celebrated the festival in the woods. That was the beginning of the *Linka* Festival of Shigatse.

TIBETAN ART

Historically, one of Tibet's primary trade products was its beautiful wool carpets. Brightly patterned in traditional Tibetan, Chinese, and Indian motifs, they are woven on simple looms and used for clothes, blankets and seat covers. The weave is trimmed around the pattern to emphasise the design, and it is made from Tibetan wool where available.

However, much Tibetan art is deeply religious in nature, from the exquisitely detailed metal and earth statues found in temples and monasteries and wooden carvings on buildings to the intricate designs of *thangka* paintings and sand mandalas, even down to the beautifully decorated butter carvings created by lamas in monasteries for the New Year.

Thangka painting

Thangka paintings are traditional Tibetan paintings of a Buddha, Buddhist deity, or a mandala. Although *thangkas* are framed in rich, colourful silk brocades, they are not simply decorations but religious objects. They can be found in every monastery and family shrine in Tibet. Devotees reflect on the work, identifying and developing within themselves the qualities such as wisdom and compassion that are embodied in the painting.

While they are termed "paintings", *thangka* can be classified into several types — painted, embroidered, and woven, among others, though the painted *thangkas* are the most common. A combination of Chinese scroll-painting, Nepalese painting and Kashmir painting, they first appeared around the 10th century and are usually rectangular in shape, painted on cotton or linen with mineral and organic pigments and finally mounted on a colourful silk background. Exceptional *thangkas* may use ground gold and gemstones as pigments. *Thangka* subjects cover many fields, from astrology to medicine to theology, including mandalas and images of Buddhas.

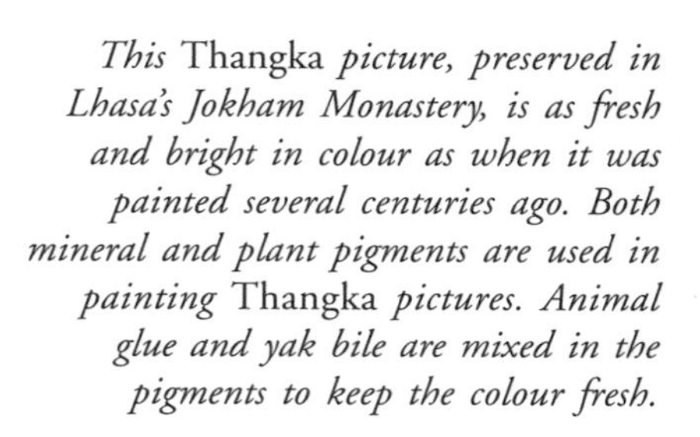

This Thangka *picture, preserved in Lhasa's Jokham Monastery, is as fresh and bright in colour as when it was painted several centuries ago. Both mineral and plant pigments are used in painting* Thangka *pictures. Animal glue and yak bile are mixed in the pigments to keep the colour fresh.*

Thangka painting is governed by strict rules. An artist must spend many years as an apprentice, drawing and studying ancient texts under a master. This apprenticeship teaches not only the technical skills required for the meticulously detailed work, but also, during this time, the artist actively seeks spiritual calm and moral fortitude. As part of this process, *thangka* painters of old observed disciplines such as abstaining from meat, alcohol, onions and garlic, as well as maintained strict personal cleanliness.

Traditionally, *thangkas* are commissioned by religious devotees, but today, *thangkas* are produced in bulk for tourist markets in Nepal, India, and elsewhere.

TIBETAN ARCHITECTURE

Tibetan architecture is simple in structure and colour, adapted to the harsh climate. The houses, typically built on elevated sunny sites facing south, are made of stone, wood and earth. They have flat roofs to conserve heat, and many windows for light as there are few fuel sources to burn. Walls slope inwards as a precaution against earthquakes.

There are family niches in every house for keeping Buddha images. Woollen blankets serve as mattresses and cushions, and quilts are made of sheepskin or wool. The nomadic herders live in tents made from yak hair and use their voluminous gowns in place or mattresses and quilts.

Prayer flags can be found fluttering on tents, rooftops, hilltops, and almost anywhere you can find a Tibetan. They signify fortune and good luck.

The Potala* Palace

On the sacred Putuo Hill above Lhasa, the capital of Tibet, there is a palace within a palace, of red, white, and gold, built on the ruins of another palace that was built a thousand years earlier by the legendary Tibetan king, Songtsen Gampo.

Rising majestically from the mountains, the Potala Palace is a marvel of Tibetan architecture that throws all other mundane structures almost literally into its shadow. Thirteen storeys high, with over 1,000 rooms, it towers more than 110 metres above the ground and measures some 300 metres from end to end. This is the palace of the Dalai Lamas, built by the order of the fifth Dalai Lama, who did not live to see its completion. Work began in 1656, and 7,000 workers took almost 50 years to finish the inner Red Palace.

The Potala Palace comprises the White Palace and the Red Palace, based on the colour of the walls. The rooms within are gorgeously decorated with murals, paintings, wood and stone carvings, and gold and silver ornaments.

* *Sanskrit for Buddha's Mountain.*

The outer White Palace served mainly pragmatic functions, containing living quarters, administrative offices, the seminary and a printing house with hand-carved wooden blocks for the press. The spiritual centre of the complex was the Red Palace, housing the monks' assembly hall, chapels, 10,000 shrines, as well as vast libraries of Buddhist scriptures. The embalmed remains of the Dalai Lamas are kept in the great Hall of Sacrifice, in elaborate funerary pagodas.

Even discounting its historic and architectural significance, the Potala Palace is a place of wonders, collecting within its walls uncountable works of art, a maze of painted galleries, richly decorated prayer rooms and almost 200,000 priceless statues. Butter lamps are constantly kept burning, and today, the grand palace serves as a museum and shrine, a monument to Tibet's rich cultural heritage.

TIBETAN OPERA

Tibetan folk opera, or *lhamo*, is said to have been created in the 14th century by Drupthok Thangthong Gyalpo, a monk and bridge builder. Supposedly, he organised the first performance with the help of seven pretty girls to raise funds for building bridges to facilitate transportation. The tradition continued, developing into its current form, and *lhamo* performances are now held on various festive occasions.

The repertoire is drawn from Buddhist stories and Tibetan history. Performances, held on a bare stage, begin with the purification of the stage and a blessing. A narrator sings a summary of the story in verse, and brightly costumed performers enter. The drama is a combination of dances, chants and songs, and the role of the performer can be identified by the colour of the mask, with red for the king, green for the queen, and yellow for lamas and deities. The chorus is sung by all the performers, and there may be spoken improvisations that reflect contemporary concerns and make fun of authority figures. The performance ends with another ritual of blessing.

The best time to see the operas would be during the 10-day festival held in Norbu-Linka, in which performers from all over Tibet come to perform.

Xuedun Festival
(*Shoton*, the Yogurt Festival)

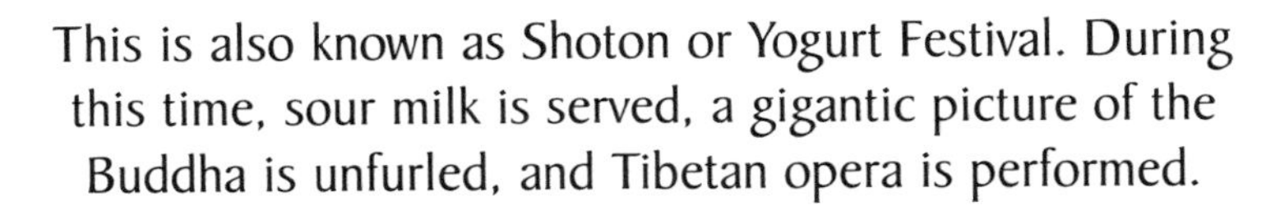

This is also known as Shoton or Yogurt Festival. During this time, sour milk is served, a gigantic picture of the Buddha is unfurled, and Tibetan opera is performed.

Ma, why are you preparing so much yogurt?
It's the *Xuedun* Festival today.

Xue means sour milk, and *dun* means to offer.

Have a bowl first.

Gobble, gobble...

Wow, it's very good!

Xuedun Festival is the day of offering sour milk.

Before the 17th century, Xuedun was a purely religious activity.
The 15th to the 30th day of the sixth lunar month is a time of growth for all living things. It is also a period of strict restraint for the followers of the Gelugpa Order.
Do not leave the monastery during this time as you might accidentally step on insects and commit sin by killing.
The monks remained in the monastery to cleanse their souls. They would pass the days peacefully.

The restriction was lifted on the first day of the seventh lunar month.
It was a time when flowers bloomed and the yaks were strong.
Milk produced by the cows was good and plentiful. The yogurt made at this time was most fragrant and delicious.
The herdsman offered the monks the yogurt. This is the origin of the *Xuedun* Festival.
Master, have a bowl.

In 1642, the Gelugpa Order dominated Tibet and the fifth Dalai Lama came into power.

On the 30th day of the sixth lunar month, thousands of devotees would visit the temples to offer yogurt to the fifth Dalai Lama and the monks.

The fifth Dalai Lama touched the heads of the devotees and blessed them with good fortune, long life and bumper harvests. The Dalai Lama's blessing was an assurance that they would not be sent to Hell after death.

There was dancing and the actors dressed as yaks to perform.
The yearly celebrations evolved and became known as the *Xuedun* Festival.

Over time, Tibetan opera became the chief programme of the *Xuedun* Festival. Thus, the festival is also known as the Tibetan Opera Festival.
The new batch of Iron Pole Lamas is taking over the duties of the old batch today.
What are Iron Pole Lamas?
They are an awe-inspiring lot.
Standing absolutely straight, each holds an iron pole in his hand, looking truly formidable. All the three great monasteries in Lhasa have these lamas. But the most awe-inspiring and powerful of all are those from Drepung.
Legend has it that it was the fifth Dalai Lama who bestowed the powers on the Iron Pole Lamas.

An Iron Pole Lama patrolling the streets.
With every step he took, he hit the ground with a loud thud.

They had authority over the lamas in the monastery as well as the common folk. Each year during the 21-Day Holy Conference, the senior officials in Lhasa had to hand over power to them. They were Lhasa's real masters during this time.
I didn't know the Iron Pole Lamas were so powerful.
Will they beat kids?
Of course. If you're disobedient, they will punish you.
Bang!

The Iron Pole Lamas are coming! Help!
Look carefully before you start screaming.
Oh, it's you, Pa.
?

Let's go to Drepung Monastery to look at the long drape of the Buddha (*thangka*).

The celebration of *Xuedun* Festival begins with devotees looking upon the huge drape of the Buddha at Drepung Monastery. This takes place on the 30th day of the sixth Tibetan lunar month.

Da...da...da...

Da...da...da...

Pa, what are they carrying?
The Buddha.
The lamas carry the huge scroll of the Buddha to the platform. Devotees surround the platform, looking forward to the sacred moment.
What is the Buddha like?
You'll see in a while.
Da...di...da...

As the lamas chant the scriptures and play the *suona,* the drape is slowly unfurled.

Oh, the Buddha!

Pa, I can't see anything.
I'll give you a piggy-back.

Wow, it's huge!

The devotees are completely stunned by the huge dignified portrait of the Buddha. They go down on their knees and prostrate themselves on the ground.
Who is the one looking at the blue sky day and night?
Who is the one yearning for the eternal vision?

Chanting voices roll like the waves.
The dignity that can never be changed.
Oh... I see mountain ranges, Rivers between mountains, Rivers are joined...

Aah... That is the Tibetan plateau!

The music of the *qin*, the beat of the drums, the song, dance and laughter all mingle together. The spirit of celebration fills the palace. The brilliant display of the actors pushes the *Xuedun* Festival to a climax. The monks and the common folk share the joys and, with warmth and passion, express their wishes and hopes for a perfect and beautiful life.

THE MONKEY AND THE SHE-DEMON

Long before Charles Darwin put forward his Theory of Evolution, the Tibetan people had already claimed their descent from a monkey. There are several myths about their origins, but the most popular one since the advent of Buddhism traces their ancestry to a divine monkey who married a she-demon and had six children with her.

These children reproduced until there were five hundred of them and there was not enough fruit for them to eat. Seeing his children starving, the first monkey appealed to Guanyin, who threw down the five cereals for them to cultivate. Over time, they lost their tails and began to speak.

Traditionally, this happened near Tsethang, in the centre of the main provinces of U and Tsang, known collectively as U-Tsang. The caves of these ancestral monkeys can still be seen in the mountain called Gongpori, behind Tsethang.

(Note: In the seventh century, Princess Wencheng found through astrology that Tibet was like a female demon lying on her back, and thus many temples were built on sites corresponding to her arms, hands, legs and feet in order to lessen her power.)

The she-demon and the monkey.

THE TIBETAN CALENDAR

Until the 11th century, the Tibetan calendar was based on the Chinese calendars which the Princess Wencheng brought with her in the 7th century. Around that time, Indian Buddhists coming to Tibet brought their own version of both Buddhism and the calendar, which the Tibetans fused with the Chinese ones into a uniquely Tibetan form. The Tibetan calendar in its present form owes more to later adaptations from the Han-dynasty calendar.

The calendar was used for three main purposes: one, to provide a working seasonal schedule for farmers and shepherds; two, to find the date of Buddha's enlightenment, as it is said that Buddhism would last for 5,000 years; and three, to compute solar and lunar eclipses, as there was a complete lunar eclipse on the day of enlightenment.

Like the Chinese calendar, the Tibetan calendar has a 60-year cycle that is based on the cycles of both the sun and the moon, with the year based on the position of the sun, and the month based on the moon. Each month has 29 or 30 days, so a lunar year would have only 354 or 355 days, 11 days short of the solar year. Therefore, a "leap" month is added every few years, based on the precise Chinese astronomical calculations. As a result of differences in deciding the length of months, the New Year in the Tibetan calendar is either on the same date as the Chinese calendar, a day late, a month late, or a day and a month late.

The years are counted in 60-year cycles, divided by yin and yang (always alternate years and thus often omitted), the five elements of fire, earth, iron, water and wood, and the twelve animals of the zodiac.

Current Tibetan almanacs forecast the coming year's general climate as well as natural phenomena like droughts, blizzards and earthquakes.

DIVINATION

Divination, while existing prior to the advent of Buddhism, has been incorporated into the sphere of Buddhist concepts, so rather than being considered an alien remnant of the past, it functions in accordance with Buddhist principles such as karma. By looking into a person's future, the diviner can assess the situation and make recommendations to best affect the future. There are many varieties of divination, with tools such as dice, dough balls and prayer beads, or based on environmental signs and dreams.

Tibetan astrologers at Men-Tse-Khang study for five years. They use calculations and computers to determine an individual's lifespan as well as his or her present and future physical condition and economic status. They give consultations at births, deaths, marriages, and in the case of long illnesses. They also advise people on auspicious days to begin and end spiritual practices, travel, and conduct business. If the outlook is unfavourable, the astrologers will prepare an antidote in the form of a prayer, amulet or religious practice.

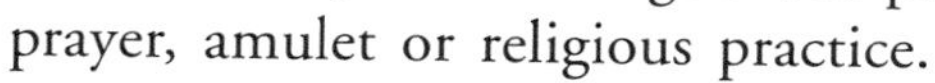

TIBETAN MEDICINE

Tibetan medicine is one of the oldest medical traditions in the world, dating back to 2,500 years ago. One of the key figures in its development is the renowned eighth century physician, Yutok Yonten Gonpo, who produced the Four Medical Tantras, which integrated material from the medical traditions of China. India, Nepal and Persia into the Tibetan corpus. His descendant, Yuthok, further consolidated the tradition with his addition of 18 medical works on it.

According to the Tibetan tradition, health is based on the balanced interaction of the five elements of earth, air, fire, water and space, a disruption of which will result in illness. Good health depends on a proper balance of diet, behaviour and environment, even including psychological and social factors. Diagnosis involves an interview, urine analysis by colour and odour, and a pulse reading. Once the nature of the illness has been ascertained, the patient can then be treated by herbal or mineral medicine, or physical therapies like acupuncture and bleeding. Long-term healthcare then depends on both lifestyle and diet.

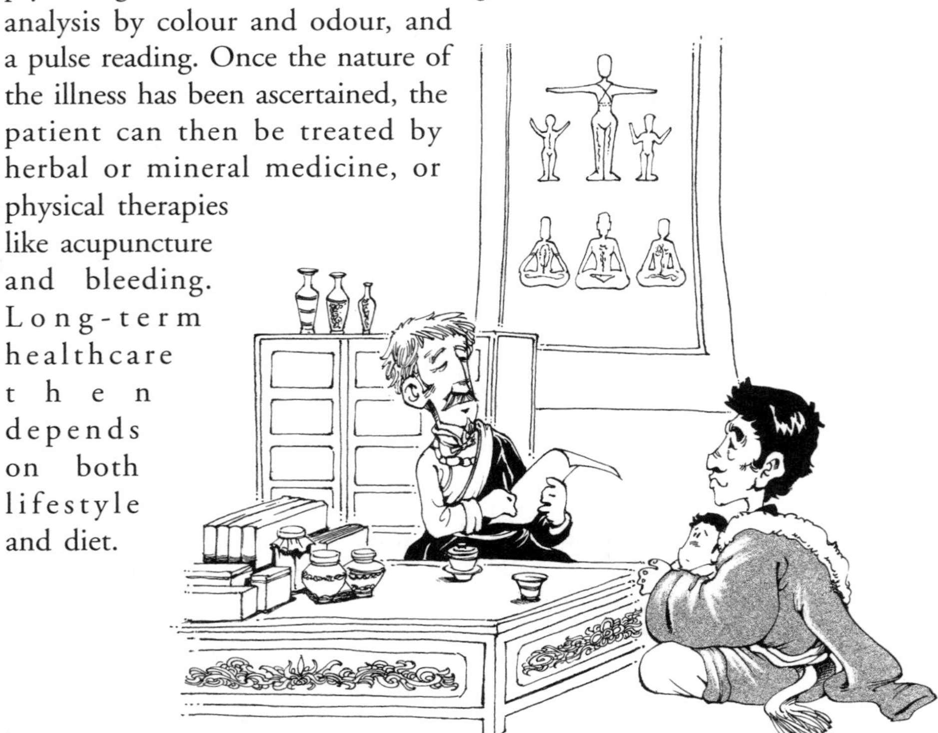

The Bathing Festival

During the Bathing Festival, Tibetans set up tents along rivers and bathe themselves in the water. They believe that the water contain medicinal qualities during this time.

One night during the seventh lunar month in Lhasa, the people looked up into the skies in the direction of the southeast.

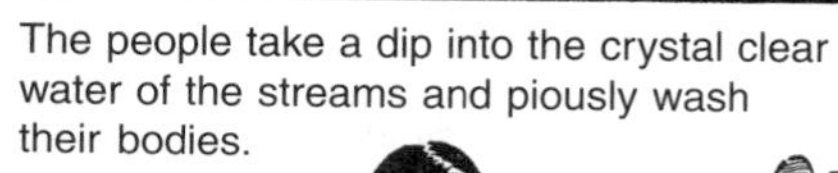

It is believed that during the Bathing Festival, the water in the rivers can get rid of pain and illnesses, enabling the body to function better.

In ancient times, there were no physicians in the mortal world. All physicians were sent to earth by the gods in Heaven.
They treated the illnesses of the impoverished Tibetan people, who lived a hard life.
When they died of old age, they returned to the heavens where they would be rejuvenated.

Cough…

Pa, lie down. Don't expose your back to the cold.

Grandpa, get up and have a bowl of hot tea.

No… No…
I don't think I'll make it.

Yixi, you'll be left with your Ma in future.

Pa, don't say that. Lord Buddha will protect you.

Plop!

Buddha, please open your eyes and save my grandpa. Please save my grandpa!

Buddha...
Tok, tok...

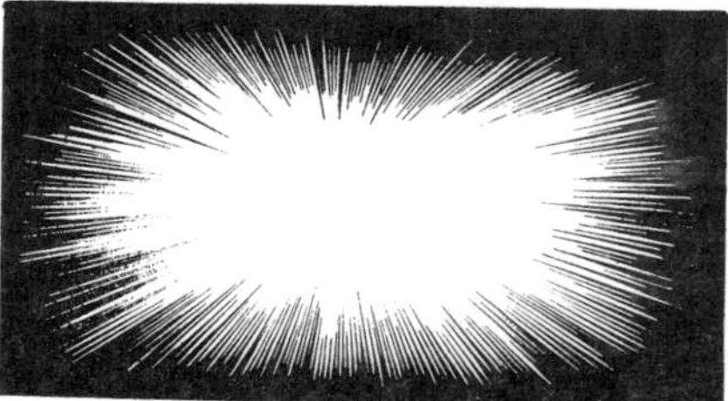

Little girl, I'll cure your grandpa.
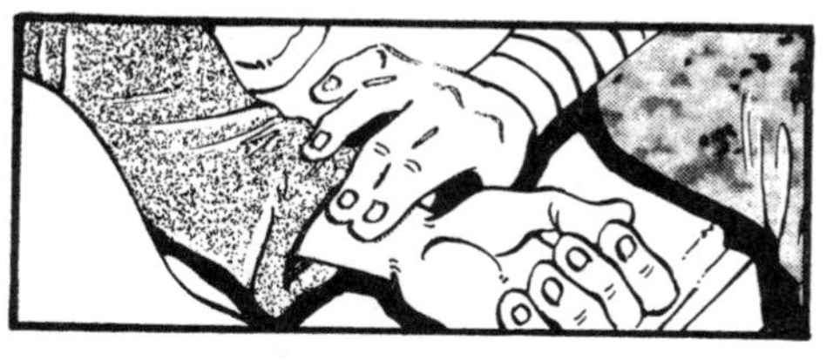

Old sir, your condition started with a chill.

Here, swallow this pill.

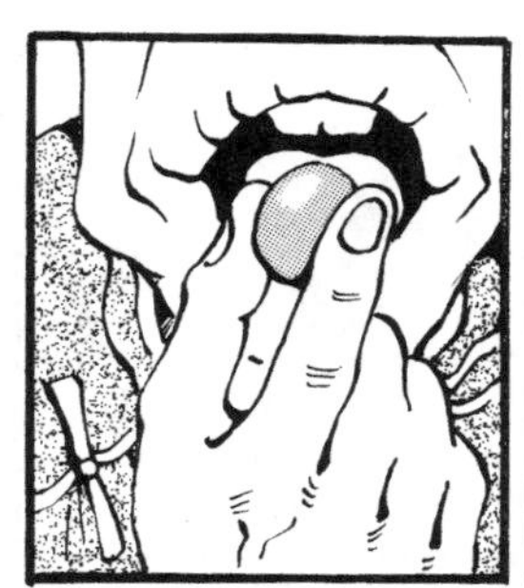

...
...

Don't worry, old sir. You'll recover in no time.

Wheee...

Wow! He disappeared in the blink of an eye!

I'm not coughing anymore and the pain is gone.

Yes, I remember now!
It must be the gods from Heaven who sent him to treat my illness. He's the Medicine Buddha.

Lord Buddha has answered our prayers. Thank you, Heaven.

The Medicine Buddha went everywhere to heal the sick and ease their pain.
He was loved by the people and was respectfully referred to as Menlha (the Medicine Buddha).

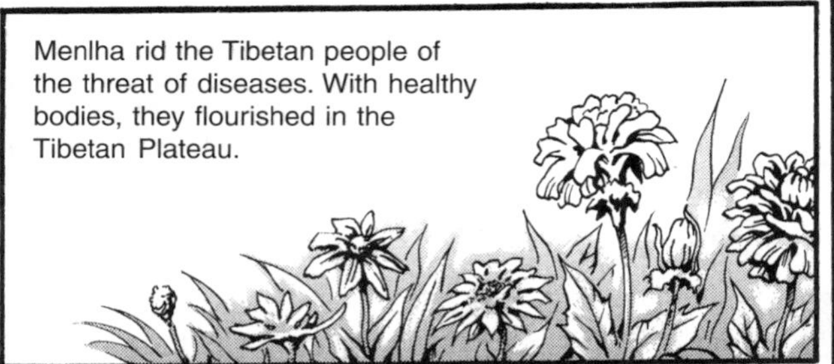
Menlha rid the Tibetan people of the threat of diseases. With healthy bodies, they flourished in the Tibetan Plateau.

Dead bodies lay everywhere on the grassland.

When Menlha returned to Heaven, a terrible plague struck the land.

Medicine Buddha, Menlha, please open your wise eyes and look at the tragedy that has befallen us.
Please come back to earth to help us!

Please save us!

Save us…

Hmm…
I think I hear someone calling for help.

Menlha walked to the Heavenly Well and looked down.

He was very sad when he saw the terrible situation on earth.
He immediately reported it to the Supreme God.
Supreme God, a plague has broken out in the grasslands. Many have died as there are no doctors to treat them.
Please allow me to return to earth so that I could make them healthy.

It was impossible to heal thousands of people in just seven days and nights. Menlha thought about it long and hard.

He transformed himself into a star that possessed the powers to heal and his love for the people. The bright rays of the star shone upon the snowy regions.
That night, a young girl in Lhasa who was on the verge of death had a strange dream.
In the dream, she saw the Medicine Buddha, Menlha, standing on top of Baoping Mountain sprinkling medicines on earth.

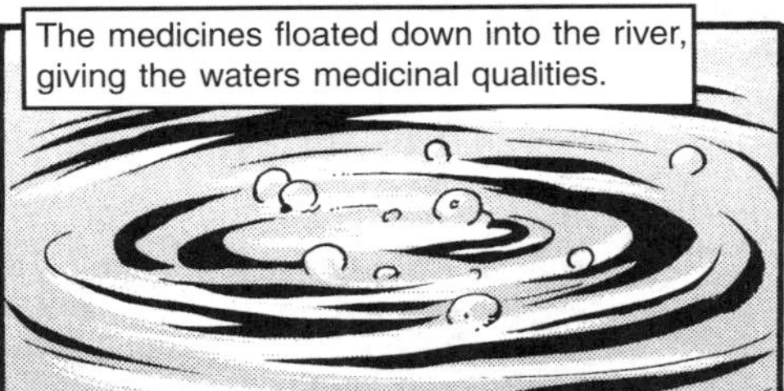
The medicines floated down into the river, giving the waters medicinal qualities.

The girl struggled up and came to the river.

She immersed her whole body into the water and made a miraculous recovery. In a second, every sign of her illness was gone.

Her tired and weak body became strong and full of life.
Her dry and wrinkled skin became fair, clear and radiant. Her dull eyes became bright and piercing.

The girl revealed what had happened. Soon, all the sick people flocked to the rivers and lakes, and began washing themselves earnestly. The plague was eradicated and the pain ended.

Relieved of their suffering, the people cheered and kowtowed to the Medicine Buddha. They prayed that his light would shine upon them every year and heal all the sick and wounded souls.

The Medicine Buddha transformed himself into the Gematuiba Star. The star appears above the peak of Baoping Range in early autumn every year. After shining for seven days, it would reluctantly disappear.

THE ADVENT AND DEVELOPMENT OF TIBETAN BUDDHISM

The first seven kings of Tibet were believed to have descended from the sky and returned there after their death, so no tombs for them was ever found. They, and the kings that followed them until the reign of the 28th king, Lhatotori Nyentsen, followed the native animistic Bon religion, which was governed by exorcists, shamans and priests.

The first Buddhist scriptures mysteriously appeared in Tibet during that time, and were thus thought to have descended from the sky. No one could read the book of scriptures, written in Sanskrit, as there was no written language at the time. However, the king dreamt that four generations on, there would be a king who would be able to read and understand the sacred text.

The 33rd king, Songtsen Gampo, ascended the throne at the age of 13 in AD 630. Under his reign, the capital of Tibet was moved to Lhasa, and Tibet emerged as a powerful military presence as he made war on the neighbouring countries of India, Tang-dynasty China, and the Turkish empire. He sent a minister to the Nepalese king to ask for the hand of Princess Bhrikuti Devi, which was granted, and marched his army into China to demand the Princess Wencheng in marriage. These two princesses brought with them images of the Buddha, and their faith proved to be a major influence on the young king.

Songtsen Gampo.

Both princesses had temples built for their images of the Buddha, and in order to translate the mysterious scriptures, the king knew a written language was required. He sent his minister, Thonmi Sambhota, with 18 companions to India, where they learnt the language from the well-known Buddhist masters, Lipi Kara and Devavidyasimha. The 18 fellow students died there, but Thonmi Sambhota returned, and used his new-found knowledge to devise a Tibetan script with 30 consonants and four vowels. While local dialects exist, this writing system is used by all Tibetans.

A close-up of the butter scripture Princess Wencheng Coming to Tibet, *which can be found in the Kumbum Monastery.*

Princess Wencheng.

The scriptures were finally translated, and Songtsen Gampo codified new laws for the nation based on its teachings, with punishments for murder, adultery and robbery. He encouraged learning of the 16 righteous duties, set official posts, defined military and administrative areas, and created a unified system of weights and measures.

Songtsen Gampo died in AD 649. In spite of his many accomplishments as a legislator, a conqueror and a religious and educational reformer, and the many temples he built, the Bon religion remained a strong presence. The two religions have adapted and assimilated many of each other's practices over the years.

There are four main Buddhist sects, and several other minor traditions, which can be generally divided into two principal schools of thought, the older school being based on the first translations of the scriptures from the seventh century, and the later based on the new translations begun after the 11th century. These two schools can be distinguished by the colour of the hats worn by the members on ceremonial occasions: red for the older non-reformed schools and yellow for the later reformed schools.

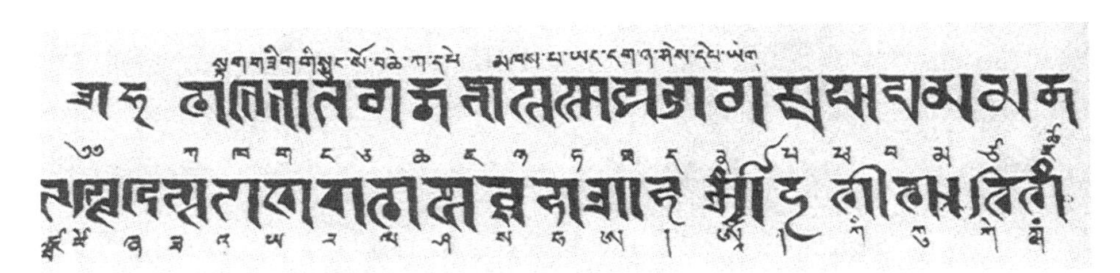

A sample of Tibetan writing.

Despite the sectarian divisions, there is little religious conflict as the members are distributed fairly evenly throughout Tibet and the teachings differ little. Tibetans tend to identify themselves as being inside the Buddha's Law rather than by sect, and pay respect to all the different schools.

The Miraculous Six-syllable Mantra

In Tibet, there are colourful prayer flags and inscriptions of the six-syllable mantra everywhere. The people spin prayer drums and carry handy prayer wheels.

Om mani padme hum…

Grandma, what are you chanting?

I said om mani padme hum.

Om mani padme hum… What does that mean?
It's an incantation in Tibetan Buddhism often referred to as the six-syllable mantra.

It means "Hail to Buddha in the Lotus".

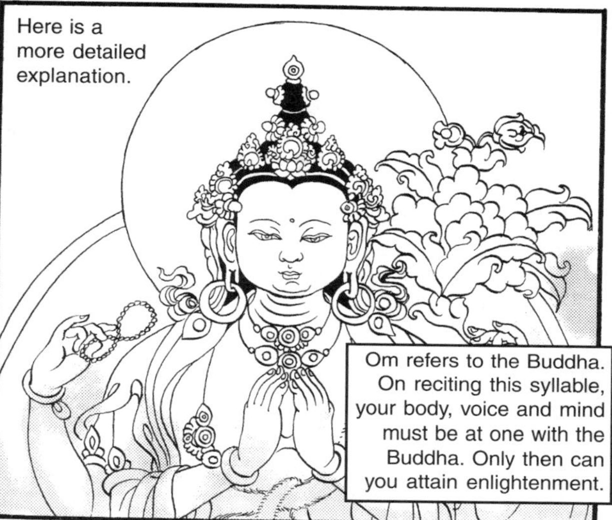
Here is a more detailed explanation.
Om refers to the Buddha. On reciting this syllable, your body, voice and mind must be at one with the Buddha. Only then can you attain enlightenment.

Ma-ni refers to the Ruyi Treasure (good-luck charm), also known as the Mani Treasure. Legend has it that the treasure was hidden in the brain of the Dragon King. The one who possessed it would have the key to the treasures from all over the land. Thus, it is also called Jubao (the gathering of treasure troves).
Pad-me refers to the lotus. It is a metaphor for the teachings of Buddha, which remain pure and untainted like the spotless lotus, unsoiled by the mire from which it grows.

Hum refers to Vajrakumara (a meditational Buddha). It is said in prayer in the quest for enlightenment. The path to salvation can only be attained through the powers of Buddha.

Why do some people keep chanting it all day?

Chanting the mantra over and over can ward off disasters, increase your merits and lead you to the path of enlighten-ment.
When misfortunes or illness befall you, chanting the mantra will help you through the crisis.

If things haven't been going well for you, chant the mantra to lighten your heart.
Really? I'll give it a try.

Om mani padme hum... Ha ha...

The old lady and her grandchild came to a mani pile.

What's engraved on it?

Om mani padme hum.

People expressed their hopes for happiness and their respect for the Buddha by carving the six-syllable mantra on the slab.

Grandma, the banners have these six words too.
These banners with Buddhist scriptures written on them are called prayer flags.
The different colours of the prayer flags symbolise different things.
Blue symbolises the sky; white, the clouds; red, fire; green, water; and yellow, the earth.
The flags flutter in the wind. Every flutter represents our sincerity, praise and devotion to the gods.

Soon, the old woman and her granddaughter came to a temple.

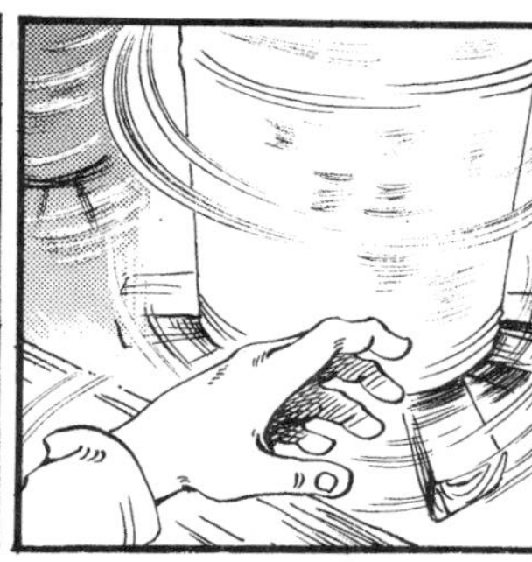

Grandma, these round drums are nice to play with.

These are not toys. They're prayer drums.

One revolution of the drum is equal to chanting the sutra once.

Grandma, when did the six-syllable mantra appear in Tibet?
Er... It must be a long time ago.

This prayer wheel I'm holding is the same as the prayer drum. Turning it repeatedly is as good as reciting the sutra again and again.

How long ago is that?

Let's ask a guru.

The old woman and her grandchild posed the question to a guru.
The six-syllable mantra first appeared during the reign of King Lhatotori Nyentsen.

It was said that one day, King Lhatotori dreamt of a treasure falling from Heaven.

Though he did not quite believe his dream, he instructed his men to make a search. On the palace roof, a treasure chest was found.

The chest contained a Buddhist sutra, some mantras and religious objects.

The written word was not yet created in Tibet in those early days. No one knew what was written in the sutra.

It was not only until Songtsen Gampo's time (around the middle of the seventh century), when the country invited monks to the land, that the sutra was translated.
Buddhism began to spread in Tibet from then on and the chanting of the six-syllable mantra spread among the people.
The meritorious deed of worshipping the Buddhas can be measured, but chanting the six-syllable mantra is a meritorious deed that is beyond measure.
Nowhere in Tibet would you not see the six-syllable mantra and the colourful prayer flags. The chant of the mantra moves even the universe.

Rebirth of the Living Buddha

In Buddhism, there is a belief that the soul cannot be destroyed, but is reborn. This belief does not only apply to the common folk.

The rebirth of the living Buddha is one of the special characteristics of Tibetan Buddhism.
It is also a religious system based on economic considerations to settle the succession problem of religious leaders.

The belief that famous lamas can be reincarnated after death originated from the Karmapa Order. Gradually, it became widely adopted by other monasteries in Tibet and became the foundation of the Gelugpa Order.

May 1876. It had been a year since the 12th Dalai Lama passed away. To find the child who was the reincarnation of the Dalai Lama, the advice of the eighth Panchen Lama was sought.

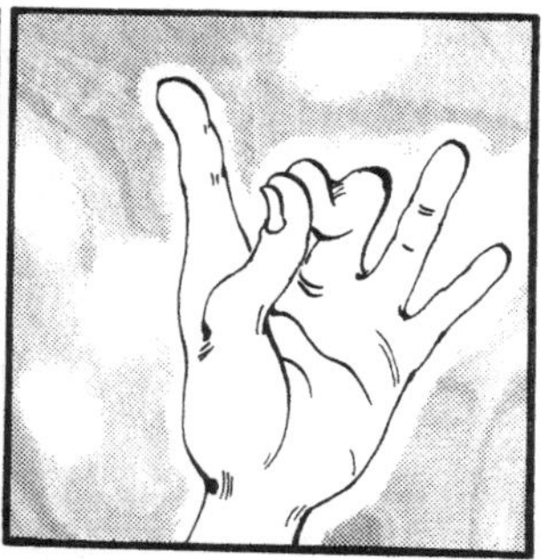

The Dalai Lama has been reborn.

The child lives in a village to the southeast of Lhasa. His father's name is Gongga Renqing, and his mother's name is Zhuoma. We should have our people go in search of him.

Thank you, Guru Panchen.

Following the clues given by Guru Panchen, the monks went to the sacred lake to check the reflection.
It was a belief in Lamaism that when religious rites were performed at a specific lake, a vision of the child and the place he lived in would appear.

The monks came to the lakeside and began the rites.

As they chanted and prayed, they threw objects like the *hada*, vases and herbs into the water.

Wow, the vision has appeared!

The lamas began a long search based on the drawing. Finally, one day…

Let's ask him.
All right.

Is this Langdun Village?
Yes.

Do you know someone called Gongga Renqing?

Why do you wish to see me?

You're the one?

This is great! We've found you.

Koochi koochi ...
Now, give me a smile.

Smile.
Smile at Mama.

Masters, please come in.

Zhuoma, open the door.

Have a seat. Zhuoma and I will prepare some tea for you.

Look at the child.

Is this child the reincarnation of the Dalai Lama?

What? Our son is the reincarnation of the Dalai Lama?
Shh… Not so loud. It's just a possibility.
Om mani padme hum…
Oh, merciful Buddha!

The 12th Dalai Lama used one of the 12 objects here. If the child picks the object, it'll prove he was the Dalai Lama in his previous life.
Boy, pick an object.

Gurgle…

Gongga, Zhuoma, the test has shown that your child is the reincarnation of the 12th Dalai Lama. Congratulations.
You must take good care of him from now on. Do not let strangers go near him.
Thank you, masters.
We'll see to it.

When the child was found, the eighth Panchen Lama, the Regent, and the other monks formally requested Emperor Guangxu to have a gold vase made.
The gold vase served to prevent the lamas in power from resorting to corrupt practices when the child was found. The child's name and date of birth were written on the sticks in the Han, Tibetan and Manchurian languages. When that was done, they were placed in the vase.
Wise and learned lamas prayed for seven days. At Jokhang Monastery, the sticks were drawn before the statue of the Buddha.

Receive the Imperial Decree! Gongga Renqing's son, Luosang Takaijiacuo, is bestowed the sticks of the Golden Vase as the vision indicated. He will succeed as the 13th Dalai Lama.
聖旨

Thank you! Long live His Majesty!
The young Dalai Lama wore the religious robe and sat on the carriage. The procession proceeded towards Lhasa. People standing on both sides of the road greeted him with joy. He was the 13th Dalai Lama, Thubten Gyatso.

FUN AND GAMES IN TIBET

Singing and dancing are an integral part of Tibetan culture, and almost any festive event or activity, be it a wedding or party, is an occasion for song and dance. They have love songs, work songs, ceremonial songs, children's songs and even wine songs and songs to divine marriage fortunes.

Tibetan children play *takchom*, an acrobatic skipping game accompanied by singing, and *tepe*, a game played with shuttlecocks of metal decorated with feathers or small sandbags, in which the *tepe* must be kept in the air as long as possible with only the inside of the foot and ankle. Adults play a dice game called *sho* with two dice, cowrie shells, and a set of markers for the respective players, or Tibetan Go (*Mi* means eyes, *mang* means many), known as "Many Eye Game" or "War Between the Eyes".

Picnics are popular in the spring, with families setting up tents by rivers and streams for several days. There is the ubiquitous music, dancing, games, picnic foods and kite-flying. They also get together outdoors to celebrate special anniversaries and religious ceremonies.

Traditional sports are horse- and yak-racing, polo, horsemanship, wrestling, archery and two-man tug-of-war, though there are now facilities for basketball, badminton, gymnastics and other modern sports.

Tibetan Traditional Sports.

Horse-racing Festival

The Horse-racing Festival is held on the first day of the eighth lunar month in the Tibetan calendar. It is a time of gaiety and celebration, with sombre origins.

Ja...
The Horse-racing Festival is a traditional event of the Huarui tribe of Tibet. It is celebrated in memory of the 13 Huarui heroes who fought in defence against the invaders.

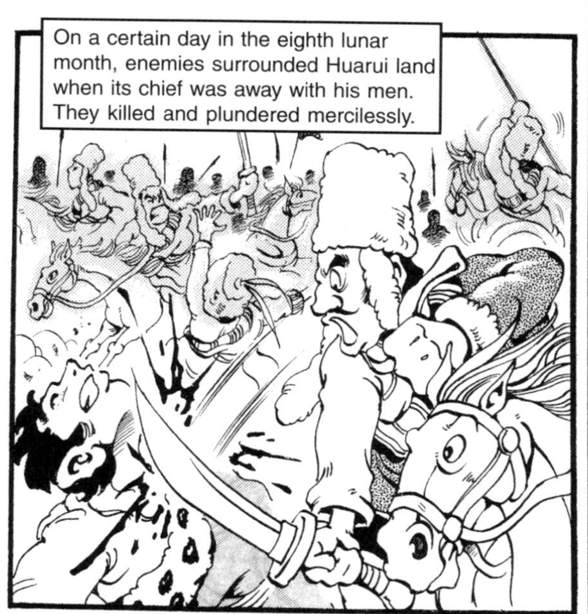
On a certain day in the eighth lunar month, enemies surrounded Huarui land when its chief was away with his men. They killed and plundered mercilessly.

Fourteen lucky survivors were trapped on the mountaintop.

We can't hold out for long. Someone has to fight his way out to bring reinforcements.

Big Brother, let me go.

I won't let you down.
Eighteen-year-old Luosang charged out by himself.

Trouble! Someone is trying to break out of the encirclement. Stop him!
Splat!
Get out of my way!

After him! Don't let him get away! Use fire to block his path.
The fire is blocking my way!
Ha! The fire has stopped him.
Slash!
Meet your doom!

You'll open a route for me!

Whack!

Ja!

Neigh!
Oh no! He's gotten away!
Go!
Clip-clop...
Lilac horse, go faster!

Whoah!

Neeeigh...

The river ahead has cut off his escape route.

Lilac horse, it's all up to you now!

Yeee...
Whaaa!

Golly! Fantastic horse! Really magical!
Fools, wake up! Fire the arrows!
Whooosh...

Aaugh!

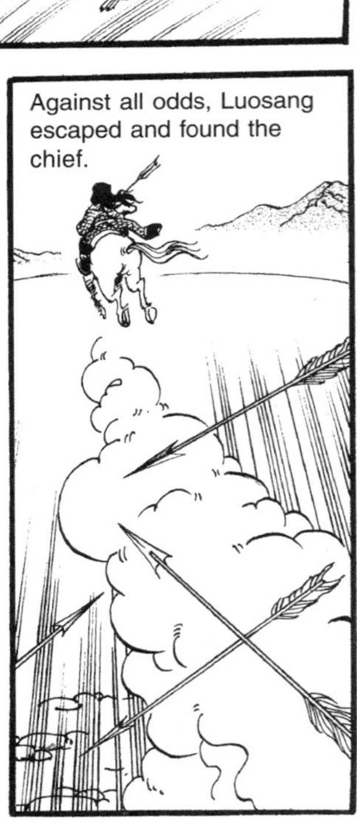
Against all odds, Luosang escaped and found the chief.

Brothers, let's return to protect our homes!
Brave Luosang accomplished what he set out to do.
Unfortunately, his horse died of exhaustion.
One by one, the 13 men on the mountaintop died, defending their homes.

The Huarui chief led 20,000 troops to avenge his brothers. With the enemy destroyed, the Huarui tribe was able to rebuild its strength.
In memory of the 13 men, the Horse-racing Festival is held in the Tibetan districts every year.
In every racing event, 13 winners are picked and rewarded to salute the indomitable spirit of the brave.

FROM BIRTH TO DEATH

A white scarf known as the *hada* is offered during almost every social occasion, be it greetings, visits to shrines, weddings or funerals. The tradition has its origins in the ancient custom of offering clothes to adorn religious images, which gradually evolved into a customary form of greeting, with the white colour symbolising purity.

Birth

The birth ceremony is called *Pangsai* in Tibetan. It is believed that babies are born alongside ills (*pan*), which must be cleared away (*sai*) by means of a special ceremony so that the babies can grow strong and the mothers recover quickly. Based on ancient Bon religious rituals, this ceremony has been in existence for more than 1,500 years.

On the third day after the birth of a boy, and the fourth day for a girl, related households come together for the ritual, bringing gifts of barley wine, butter, butter tea, meat and clothing for the newborn. As they enter the house, they present white *hada* scarves, first to the baby's parents, then the baby. This is followed by a round of toasts, presenting the gifts, and offering good wishes as they examine the baby. Some families prepare a pancake feast for the visitors.

The baby is not given a name until the end of the birth rituals. Generally, a senior villager or a high-ranking lama is invited, though some parents prefer to name their own babies.

When the baby is one month old, it must go through another ritual on an auspicious day so that it can be safely brought out of the house. Black ash is daubed on the baby's nose to ward off evil, and the baby, dressed in new clothes, is taken to the monastery to worship the Buddha and to be blessed.

Tibetan names tend to be taken from the Buddhist scriptures or place names, some of which are listed below. Tibetans usually go by their given names rather than family names, and to avoid confusion, it is common to add signifiers as "junior", "senior", a person's outstanding features, birthplace, residence or profession.

TIBETAN NAME	ENGLISH MEANINGS
Cho-kyi, Cho-kli	Possessed of Dharma (Religion) Chos = Dharma (Chos is pronounced "Chö")
Cho-nyi	Radiance (Sun) of Dharma
Da-; Da-wa	Monday, Moon (Child born on Monday)
Do-rje	Lightening Bolt, Diamond Do-rje: Do = Stone; rJe = Prince. (Prince of Stones = Diamond; i.e. Diamond Path, or Vajrayana Enlightenment)
Gyel-tsen (Gyeljen, Geljen)	Royal Courage, conqueror Gyel-tsen: gyel = king; tsen = courage
Gom-bu	Meditation
Jangbu	Wise, learned, skilful, clever
Lhak-pa	Wednesday, planet Mercury
Ming-ma (Ming-mar, Mig-mar, Mik-mar)	Tuesday, planet Mars
Nam-kha	Spacious Sky, essential space, energy of Space
Phu-dorje	Knowledge (a power of Jupiter, the day ruler) plus clarity (a quality of Diamond)
Sang-gye	(Gautama) Buddha
Tshe-wang	Powerful life
Wang-chu; Wongchu	Wang-chuk: Wang = power; chuk = holder i.e. Mighty One (Buddhist Lord of the World)

Love and Marriage

When a girl reaches 15 to 16 years, a ceremony will be held on an auspicious day, during which her hair will be plaited from a single queue to many queues and she will start wearing a colourful apron. This marks her transition into adulthood, after which she is allowed to associate freely with boys.

Any public gathering, be it horse-racing or a religious festival, is a good occasion for the sexes to meet. Young people gather to dance, sing and date one another.

If the romance is successful, the young couple ask permission from their parents to be engaged, which is usually granted. The boy or his parents will ask an old gentleman to be their matchmaker and propose the union to the girl's family with a *hada* and a bottle of barley beer. After he enters the house of the girl's family, the women will withdraw, and the proposal is accepted or declined. If the girl is willing, the bottle is opened, and the couple is considered to be engaged. The boy's family will then present suitable gifts, as well as "milking money" and aprons to the girl's parents as thanks for raising her. An auspicious date is determined for the wedding ceremony.

The couple may choose to join either family. On the evening before the wedding, the maternal uncle of the groom (or the bride, if the boy is marrying into her family. Subsequent references to the bride or groom are similarly reversed in this circumstance) comes with a white horse or other transport for the bride to ride on, a white gown, a tea-brick and butter. Beer is offered to the uncle, who will drink while on horseback, then proceed to the bride's house, where he will bless the house and the objects inside, as marrying out a child signifies a loss of wealth.

The next day, the bride will leave with one uncle from each family for the house of the groom, where a square mat of white wool has been laid out with an emblem formed from grains of barley which she must step in the middle of. The groom's uncle rides ahead to announce her arrival, while the bride's uncle opens the door with a *hada*. Both men will exchange *hada* and chant blessings.

The couple kneel in front of the groom's parents and the Buddha while monks chant. The bride then uses her ring finger to salute the heaven, earth and Buddha with milk tea, and serve milk tea to the parents.

Finally, the wedding feast begins, while guests continue to present gifts, blessings and *hadas* to the happy couple. The wedding feast(s) and gift-giving rituals may continue over a period of several days.

Most Tibetans practise monogamy, but it is not unusual for one man to have more than one wife, usually to take care of his kinsmen's widows, or if he has married into his wife's family and her sisters wish to stay in the family. Women may also have more than one husband, usually brothers, to avoid having to divide property.

Death

As Tibetan Buddhists believe in a constant cycle of death and reincarnation, the sky burial is part of the cycle of life and death, helping to redeem the sins of the deceased.

The body, wrapped in a white cloth, is kept in the house for a few days while monks are invited to chant sin-redeeming sutras. Butter lamps are lit, sometimes as many as a hundred at a time, depending on the conditions. A red jar is hung at the door of the house, decorated with a white *hada* and containing burning *tsampa* dough mixed with blood, meat, grease, milk, cheese and butter. Other families also mourn, bringing pots of wine. The day before the removal of the body,

neighbouring families bring a *hada*, incense, a sacrificial lamp and some money. The funeral itself is held early in the day. A monk leads the procession to the funeral ground, and the body carried by friends of the deceased as relatives do not go to the site.

For the first seven weeks after the death, the family avoids wearing ornaments, singing and dancing, while neighbouring families do not hold happy events, and monks are invited to chant sutras every seven days . At the end of the period, life returns to normal and their relatives bring gifts. Some families hold a mourning anniversary to thank the relatives for their assistance over the past year.

Sky Burial

When someone dies, Tibetans usually dispose of the body by feeding it to vultures. This is done for religious, moral and practical reasons.

Caw...

Woo...

Sob...
sob...

Here are four taels. Please help my brother rise to Heaven in a pure state.

Sob...
sob...
I'll carry the body up.

The body was placed at the sky burial site and the smoke of burning mulberry curled upwards.
A lama read the sutra for the dead man.
Caw...
The mulberry smoke attracted the vultures. They flew over and landed on the outcrop.

It is time.

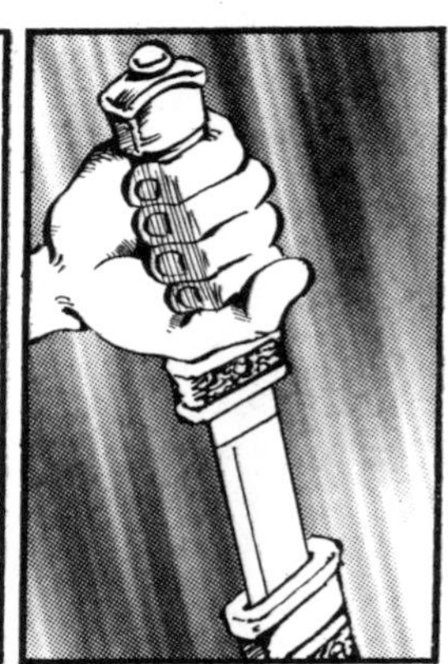

I'm the body-cutter of the sky burial ground.
I am but a lowly commoner.

My master told me not to look down on the work of a body-cutter. The sky burial ground is a sacred place and sky burial is a scared task.

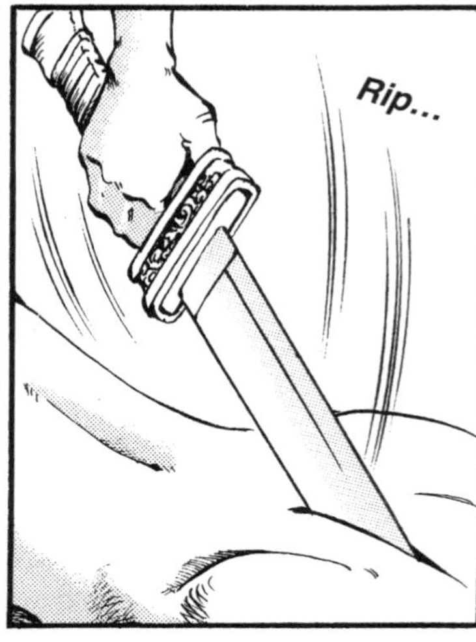
Rip...

Done!
Whistle...
Caw...
Whoosh!

They devoured the corpse so quickly!

Women are not allowed to enter the sky burial ground.
Oh dear, I'm discovered.

What?

Buddha will punish you.
I'm not afraid.

Why did you go to the sky burial site?
I wished to know what sky burial is like.

You're truly audacious, Miss.
Stop calling me Miss. My name is Jiecuomu. What's yours?
Nima.
Nima, why do some people opt for sky burial?

In his previous life, Lord Buddha, Sakyamuni, fed his body to the tigers and eagles. He was the pioneer of sky burial.
During the 11th century, Tangbasangjie, a famous monk from India, came to Tibet and founded the Xijie Order. He actively encouraged the people to adopt the practice of sky burial. At the sky burial ground, he would chant the scriptures to appease the souls of the dead. With his efforts, sky burial spread to all parts of the country.

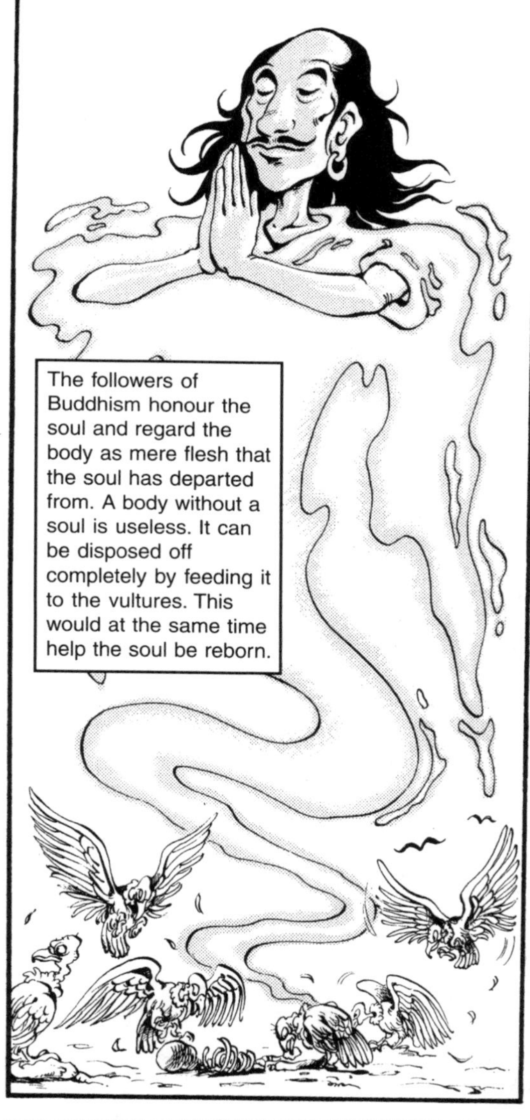

People whose corpse were offered to the vultures would have their sins atoned. Their souls would soar to Heaven with the help of the divine vultures.

If the vultures do not eat the body or eat just part of it, the family would be upset. It indicates that the deceased's sins are too great and the soul will fall into Hell.

Nima, you're really smart and know-ledgeable.
My master told me all this.

Nima, will you marry me?

No, a body-cutter is of low status. I have no house, power or money.

If you have these things, will you marry me? I have money to buy a house and livestock...
Don't be a body-cutter anymore. Take me away.

Take you away?
I can't do this. Your father will kill me if he finds out.
I'll beg him to let us be together.

No!
Out of the question!

You're the daughter of a chieftain, and he is just a lowly body-cutter. You two are not compatible.

Pa, we really love each other.

Little wretch!

Do as I say or get out of the house!

Nima, I'll walk and prostrate myself to Lhasa. I'll beg Lord Buddha to tell my father I'm your woman.

Lord Buddha, please bless Nima and me.

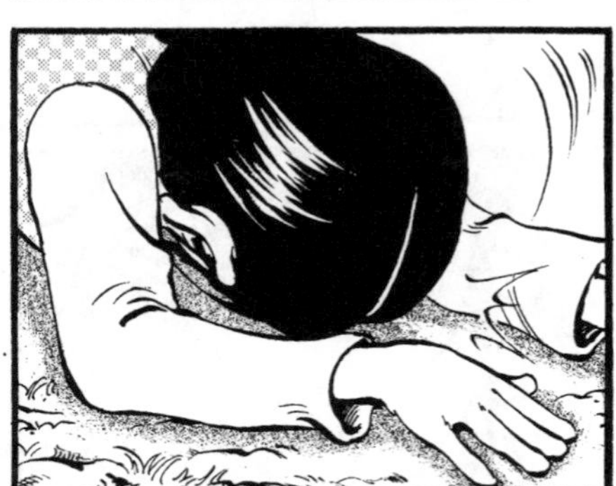

Jiecuomu, go home.
I'm going to Lhasa to seek Lord Buddha's blessing.
Are you mad? It takes at least a year for a man to walk and prostrate himself all the way to Lhasa.
You are but a vulnerable girl. It's more than a thousand li to Lhasa.
Moreover, you might run into bandits or be caught in a snow-storm.
Jiecuomu wouldn't listen to Nima and carried on.

Wait for me. I'll pack my animal-skin cloak. We'll go to Lhasa together.

Nima returned after getting his cloak. A snowstorm began to blow.

We parted here yesterday.

Huh...

Who's buried in the snow?

Jiecuomu!

Jiecuomu, wake up! It's me, Nima!

Jiecuomu, don't scare me!

Oh…

Jiecuomu!

Aaaargh!

Jiecuomu, I'll appease your soul through sky burial.
According to Master, these strokes can only be used once by the body-cutter in his lifetime.
Jiecuomu, I'll wield a beautiful, sophisticated and rhythmical set of strokes handed down by sky burial masters from the old days.

Wahhh...
Very good. They ate every morsel.
Jiecuomu, your whole body has been offered to the vultures. You'll go to Heaven soon. Go in peace. I'll remain at the sky burial site forever and pray for you.

PROVERBS

Tibetans are fond of proverbs and maxims, with lively metaphors. Some popular sayings and riddles are listed here.

Finally obliged to depart, even a king cannot take his wealth and his companions along.
But wherever he goes or stays, the results of his actions will follow him, inseparable as a shadow.
— The Four Contemplations

Rebellious thoughts are like an abandoned house taken over by robbers.
— Phadma Sangye

If sand is poured in the donkey's ear, he will shake it out.
If gold is poured in the donkey's ear, he will shake it out.
(The ignorant cannot tell the difference between what is wholesome and unwholesome.)

MAXIMS

Lazy in the morning, working late at night.

Honour a king in his own land; honour a wise man everywhere.

The wise pursue wisdom, the dull follow in blind faith.

RIDDLES

1) It goes all over the world, yet we cannot see it.

2) She eats all the best food and never gets fat.

3) It has two wings but cannot fly away.

Answers:
1. The wind. 2. A saucepan. 3. Scissors.

Photographs are from the following publications:
– Lifestyles of China's Ethnic Minorities
– Tibet: Land of Mystery
– 西藏旅游探险手册 (Tibet Tour, Exploration and Pilgrimage Handbook)
– 作家镜头 — 西藏的故事

Buddhism in Comics

The Illustrated Heart Sutra

Written in only 260 Chinese characters, the *Heart Sutra* contains the most profound wisdom in Buddhism. Here, Buddhism is presented as the wisdom of "enlightened ones" who contemplated the trials and mysteries of life.

Sayings of Buddha

This conpendium of Buddha's lessons — dynamically illuminated by Tsai Chih Chung — provides practical guidelines for disciplining the mind and behaviour.

The Illustrated Dharma Sutra

The Dharma (Law) is the body of essential truths of the universe and human life. The Buddha shows the path to spiritual cultivation in a simple way. Tsai Chih Chung's illumination of the *Dhammapada* communicates these truths and shows us how to practise them.

Origins of Zen

In this book, Tsai Chih Chung traces the origins and development of Zen in China with a light-hearted touch which is very much in keeping with the Zen spirit of absolute freedom and unbounded creativity.

Book of Zen

Zen makes the art of spontaneous living the prime concern of the human being. Tsai Chih Chung depicts Zen with unfettered versatility.

100 Buddhas in Chinese Buddhism

Lu Yanguang traces the beginnings of Buddhism and how it spread from Central Asia and India to China 2,000 years ago. This collection includes prominent figures like Sakyamuni and Maitreya, as well as those who spread Buddhism to China, Korea and Japan.

CHINESE CULTURE SERIES

Origins of Chinese People and Customs *160pp, ISBN 981-229-242-X*
This book explores the basics of life for the "descendants of the dragon", including the beginnings of the Chinese people, the origins of Chinese names, the 12 animal signs in Chinese astrology, the afterlife, social etiquette and more!

Origins of Chinese Music and Art *160pp, ISBN 981-229-243-8*
Let this book guide you through the perplexing maze of all things Chinese. Pick up interesting facts about the "Four Treasures of the Study" — the brush, ink, paper and inkstone — which form the cornerstone of Chinese culture.

Origins of Chinese Folk Arts *160pp, ISBN 981-229-264-0*
If you have an interest in Chinese folk arts, this is the book for you! Packed with many beautiful illustrations, you will find useful information on a wide range of artistic interests covering Chinese embroidery, lacquerware, paper cutting, face masks and pottery.

Origins of Chinese Martial Arts *160pp, ISBN 981-229-268-3*
This book unravels the mystery behind Chinese martial arts, or wushu, an exotic branch of traditional Chinese culture. It traces how the rough and ready brawls of Chinese cavemen matured into the polished gongfu of Shaolin and Wudang warriors.

Origins of Chinese Festivals *240pp, ISBN 981-3068-61-2*
The Chinese people have a history of 5,000 years of civilisation. Information about the origins of Chinese traditional festivals not only help us to understand the customs and everyday habits of the Chinese but also their rich cultural heritage. Many stories associated with Chinese festivals have evolved with the development of the Chinese civilisation and as a consequence have become an integral part of the Chinese culture.

Origins of Chinese Cuisine *216pp, ISBN 981-229-161-X*
Chinese cuisine is so well-known in the world that even people who know little about the country and its culture have heard about or tasted Chinese food. Nowadays, Chinese restaurants are found in all parts of the world and Chinese food is enjoyed by people with diverse eating habits and tastes.

Tales from Asia

This book unveils some of the mysteries of old Singapore – the legendary rajahs that ruled the island, the patriotism and treachery enacted in the palace atop Fort Canning Hill, the aura surrounding Redhill, Radin Mas, Kusu and Sisters Islands, and many more. You will feel a sense of reverence and awe as you witness the events that have helped shape the majestic character of the island!

This book contains 10 enchanting Asian tales that are sure to keep young readers enthralled with their humour and ingenuity. In these stories, you will get to travel across Asia and discover Asia's best-loved stories.

Feedback Form

Hello! We would like your feedback on this book. Hearing from you will help us come up with more books that readers like you will find interesting, useful and relevant. Please complete the form and send it to:
Asiapac Books Pte Ltd 996 Bendemeer Road #06-08/09 Singapore 339944.
Thank you!

Title of book: ______________________________

Purpose in reading this book: ______________________________

Did you find this book:
1. Useful? ❑ Yes ❑ No
2. Relevant? ❑ Yes ❑ No
3. Informative? ❑ Yes ❑ No
4. Easy to read ❑ Yes ❑ No

Other comments: ______________________________

____

____

Would you recommend this book to your friends? ❑ Yes ❑ No

If yes, please provide friend's name and mailing address:
Name: ______________________________
Address: ______________________________

____

If no, why not? ______________________________

What other topics would you like us to cover in the future?

____

Please provide your suggestions for improvement, if any.

____

Would you like to be on our mailing list? ❑ Yes ❑ No

Name: ______________________ Age: ____ Sex: _____
Address: ______________________________

____

Tel: ____________ Email address: ______________________

西藏文化的故事

绘画 ：冯 戈

翻译 ：吴杰欣

亚太图书有限公司出版